WOLVERINE: F...

LEADER OF THE PACK

D0351781

CONTENTS

MARVEL *POCKET BOOK* Wolverine: First Class - Leader Of The Pack

Wolverine: First Class - Leader Of The Pack. Marvel Pocketbook Vol. 2. Contains material originally published in magazine form as Wolverine: First Class 1-8. First printing 2009. Published by Panini Publishing, a division of Panini UK Limited. Mike Riddell, Managing Director. Alan O'Keefe, Managing Editor. Mark Irvine, Production Manager. Marco M. Lupoi, Publishing Director Europe. Ed Hammond, Reprint Editor. Carol Bateup, Designer. Office of publication: Brockbourne House, 77 Mount Ephraim, Tunbridge Wells, Kent TN4 8BS. MARVEL, Wolverine, X-Men and all related characters and the distinctive likenesses thereof are trademarks of Marvel Entertainment, Inc. and its subsidiaries, and are used with permission. Copyright © 2009 Marvel Entertainment, Inc. and its subsidiaries. No similarity between any of the names, characters, persons and/or institutions in this edition with those of any living or dead person or institution is intended, and any such similarity which may exist is purely coincidental. This publication may not be sold, except by authorised dealers, and is sold subject to the condition that it shall not be sold or distributed with any part of its cover or markings removed, nor in a mutilated condition. This publication is produced under licence from Marvel Characters B.V. through Panini S.p.A. Printed in Italy. www.marvel.com. All rights reserved. ISBN: 978-1-84653-098-2

YOU DON'T THINK I *WANT* TO, BUB? I'D GIVE *ANYTHING* TO STOP BEIN' AN *ANIMAL*-- TO BE *NORMAL* AGAIN!

OF COURSE YOU ARE NOT AN ANIMAL.

YOU ARE MUCH *WORSE* THAN AN ANIMAL.

AN ANIMAL DOES NOT WASTE HIS TIME WONDERING WHETHER HE IS AN ANIMAL OR NOT.

HE SIMPLY *IS.*

ANIMAL. HUMAN.

ONE. ZERO.

GOOD. BAD. THESE THINGS ARE CREATED BY THE MIND.

USE YOUR DIAMOND SWORD. PUT THESE THINGS DOWN.

YOU THINK YOU NEED THEM, BUT YOU DO NOT.

WHAT IS THIS?

KSSSHANG

CHUNK

WHAT IS THIS?

WE'RE GONNA TAKE THEM OUT *TONIGHT*--

--AND YOU'RE COMING *WITH US*, PUP.

YOU DON'T DO WHAT NEEDS TO BE *DONE* T'GET *JUSTICE* FOR OUR FALLEN BROTHERS AND SISTERS--

--THEN *YOU'RE* GONNA BE *NEXT*.

THE PACK part

WRITTEN BY
FRED VAN LENTE

ART BY
FRANCIS PORTELA

COLORED BY
ULISES ARREOL

LETTERED BY
VC'S JOE CARAMAGNA

COVER BY
WILLIAMS & ARREOLA

JOE SABINO
PRODUCTION

MARK PANICCIA & RALPH MACCH
CONSULTING

NATHAN COSBY
EDITOR

JOE QUESADA
EDITOR IN CHIEF

DAN BUCKLEY
PUBLISHER

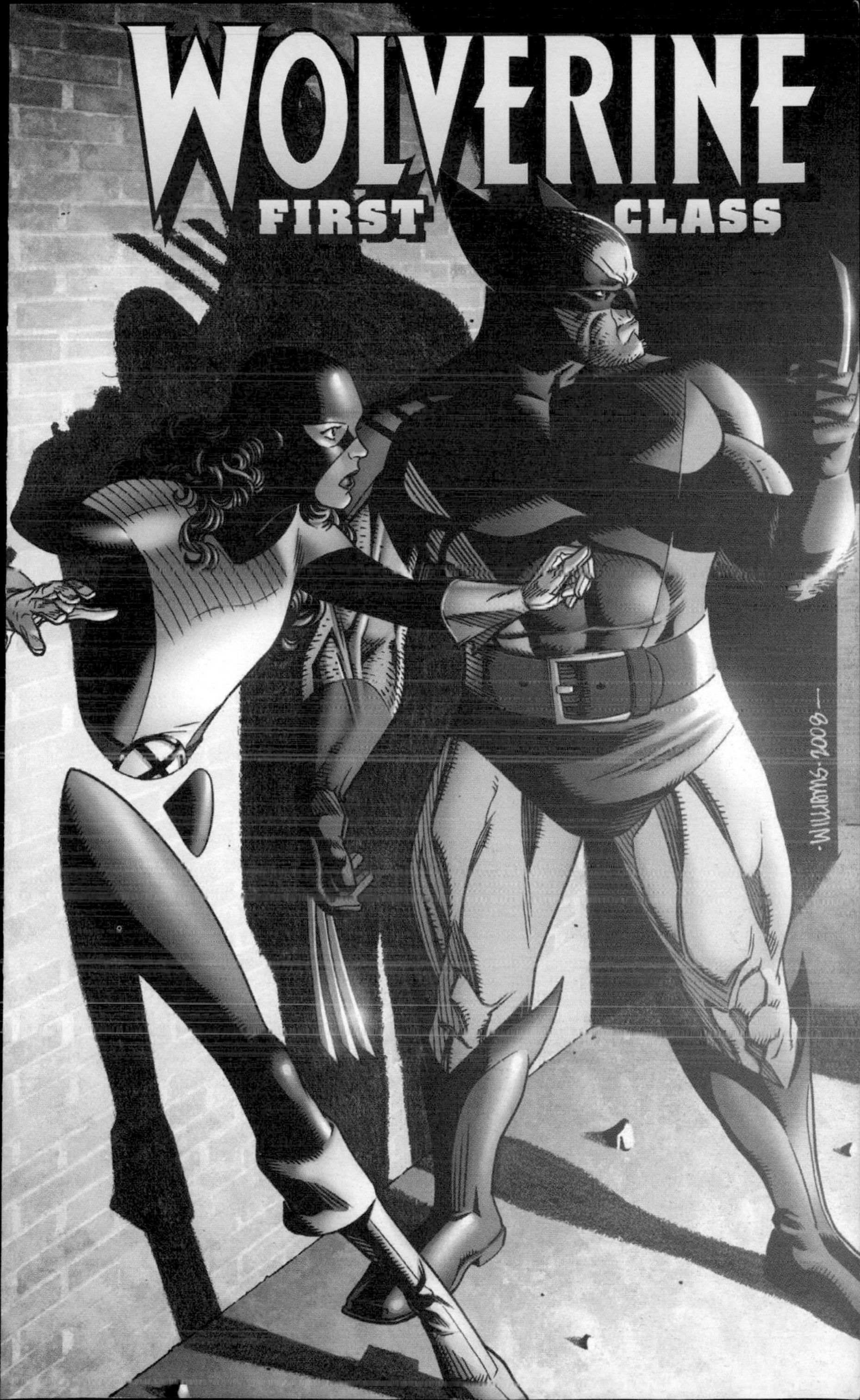
WOLVERINE
FIRST CLASS
-WILLIAMS-2008-

HE PACK part 2

WRITTEN BY
FRED VAN LENTE

ART BY
HUGO PETRUS

COLORED BY
ULISES ARREOLA

LETTERED BY
VC'S JOE CARAMAGNA

COVER BY
WILLIAMS & QUINTANA

PAUL ACERIOS
PRODUCTION

RALPH MACCHIO
CONSULTING

NATHAN COSBY
EDITOR

JOE QUESADA
EDITOR IN CHIEF

DAN BUCKLEY
PUBLISHER

AS IF HAVIN' ADAMANTIUM BONES, CLAWS, A HEALING FACTOR, AND BEIN' A FLAMIN' *SUPER HERO* WASN'T *ENOUGH.*

NOW *THIS.*

THE *CHANGE...*

SKASH

...NOT SURE HOW TO *DESCRIBE* IT, REALLY.

IT'S LIKE...YOU'RE STILL *THERE.* BUT JUST *WATCHING.* LIKE A T.V. YOU CAN'T TURN OFF.

SNIKT

SNIKT

OH, THAT'S JUST *NOT FAIR!*

RRRAAUUGGGHHH!!!!

OR *LOOK AWAY* FROM.

THE *BEAST* IS AT THE WHEEL, AND YOU'RE JUST A *PASSENGER.*

NO NO NO NO NO NO NO NO

RRROOOOAAAARR

OH THANK YOU

THANK YOU

MALIK--HE BEIN' THE LITERAL *LEADER* O' THIS PACK--SAYS HE'S TRAINED HIS CREW NOT TO HUNT *HUMANS.*

THAT'S TO KEEP THE *LAW* OFF HIS BACK-- NOT 'CAUSE HE'S ONE O' THESE BLEEDIN' HEART *"ANIMAL RIGHTS"* TYPES.

SO I KNOW THEY'RE JUST *SCARING* THESE JOE SIXPACKS.

NONE MORE THAN *NYSSA,* MALIK'S SISTER, THE DAMSEL IN NOT-SO-DISTRESS WHO GOT ME *INTO* THIS MESS IN THE FIRST PLACE.

SHE CHOSE ME AS HER *SOULMATE,* SHE *CHANGED* ME--

--OR DID SHE MAKE ME *MORE* LIKE WHAT I ALREADY *WAS?*

AND AM I *FALLING HARD* FOR HER OR FOR IT?

THE BANK STOOGE IS BEHIND ALL THIS, HUH? GIMME A NAME!

HERE-- HERE'S HIS CARD--

DEERFIELD BANK & TRUST-- JUST OUTSIDE CHICAGO--

SHUT IT DOWN, TROOPS! WE'RE DONE FOR THE NIGHT.

TO TAKE OUT A SNAKE, YOU GOTTA AIM FOR THE HEAD--

--AND NOW WE KNOW WHERE ITS NEST IS. WE HEAD THERE AT FIRST LIGHT.

WHAT DO YOU MEAN, MALIK? WHERE ARE WE GOING?

LISTEN GOOD, LOGAN. YOU'RE STILL THE PUP OF THIS PACK, AND I'M STILL THE ALPHA.

YOU GO WHERE I GO. YOU DO WHAT I TELL YOU.

WITHOUT QUESTION.

GRRRRR...

IGNORE HIM BABY. MAL[IK] WAS TOO MA[NY?] BEFORE [HE?] GOT BIT.

YOU'LL SEE. HE'L[L] ACCEPT YO[U] EVENTUALL[Y]

"...AND THEY'RE ON THEIR WAY TO CHICAGO RIGHT NOW!"

YOU AIN'T WITH A *PACK*, YOU AIN'T *NOTHIN'*.

LESS THAN NOTHIN'. YOU A *LONE*.

A LONE AIN'T GOT *NOBODY* WATCHING HIS BACK.

EVERYWHERE HE'S A *STRANGER*. EVERY FACE HIDES AN *ENEMY*.

AND IF HE HUNTS ON A TERRITORY ALREADY *CLAIMED* BY A PACK...

...HE GE MESSE UP *REA GOOD*

LIKE WHAT WE DID TO *ROL* HERE WHEN HI BLUNDERED ON OUR TURF.

HE NEARLY BOUGHT THE BIG ONE. WHEN HE *DIDN'T*, WE SAW HE COULD BE STRONG ENOUGH TO MAYBE *JOIN* US.

AS THE LOWLY *OMEGA*, THAT IS...BEFORE *YOU* CAME ALONG.

JUST 'CAUSE MY *SISTER* IS SWEET ON YOU DON'T MEAN YOU DON'T GOT TO *PROVE* YOURSELF, PUP.

I'LL KEEP IT IN MIND. HOPE THERE ISN'T ONE OF THOSE *WRITTEN* TESTS WHERE YOU GOT TO FILL IN ALL THE LITTLE CIRCLES. I *STINK* AT THOSE.

FUNNY. FUNNY LITTLE MAN--

HEY!!!

WHOOPS!

HERE, I GOT THAT--

YOU'RE DARN *RIG* YOU DO

"...IT'S ALL *DOWNHILL* FROM *THERE*."

THIRD NIGHT:

THERE! THAT'S MY HOUSE!

MOM! DAD!

GEEZ! WAIT 'TIL I PUT ON THE *BRAKES*, HUH, KID?

I'LL WAIT HERE.

PRETTY SOON... ...I WON'T BE *HOUSEBROKEN*.

DAD...?

DRAT. NO RESPONSE WHEN I CALLED FROM THE *ROAD*, EITHER...

WHERE COULD THEY HAVE *GONE...?*

HMMMM... SAY, THE DATE...

TODAY IS THEIR *ANNIVERSARY!*

AND I *COMPLETELY* FORGOT TO GET THEM SOMETHING...

THAT'S OKAY. *WE* DIDN'T.

YOU'RE THE *GIRL-CUB* OF THIS LITTLE *"PRYDE,"* HUH?

WELL, DON'T WORRY. WE DIDN'T FORGET YOU.

WE GOT *YOU* SOMETHING TOO.

MY ALPHA TOLD ME TO WAIT HERE...

NGGGGRRRAAAAHHH...

...SO I COULD GIVE IT TO YOU!

THANKS, JACK. YOU'RE STARTING TO SPECIALIZE IN SAVING MY--

RAAAHH!!!

HEY! CUT IT OUT! YOU'RE SUPPOSED TO BE *RESCUING* ME, DUMMY!

THANKS TO MY *MUTANT PHASING POWER,* YOU CAN'T *HURT* ME. SEE?

AND *JACK*-- THE, UH-- *HAIRLESS YOU*--SAID YOU SHOULD *HELP* ME FIND WOLVERINE!

RRRRRRRR???

SO *HEEL!*

SWAP

THIS *CARD* SAYS MY MOM AND DAD SPENT THE DAY IN THE CITY TO CELEBRATE THEIR ANNIVERSARY...

"...ENDING IN A *RIVER CRUISE* THROUGH *DOWNTOWN!*"

THE RATIONAL PART OF ME *KNOWS* WHAT WE'RE DOIN' IS *WRONG.*

SKAAAAAAAAASH

HOW DO YOU DO, RICH PEOPLE? I'D LIKE TO TELL YOU ABOUT TONIGHT'S SPECIALS:

YOU!

BUT REASON *SLEEPS* WHEN THE MOON *RISES.*

SO IT TAKES A COUPLE SECONDS FOR ME TO MAKE THE CONNECTION-- SINCE MY BRAIN IS WRAPPED IN *FUR.*

BUT THE *WOLF* RECOGNIZES THEIR *SCENT,* IF NOT THEIR FACES.

THE *"BANK FOOL"* AND HIS WIFE WE'RE AFTER--

THEY'RE *KITTY'S* PARENTS!

I'M DRIVING.

SNFF SNFF

I'M DRIVING.

I'M DRIVING A CAR.

RRRUURRP!!

RRROODAAAAHHHH!!

THEY'RE DOWN THERE?

YOU SURE, BOY?

WHOA--

THUMP

SKREEEEEEEEEEEEEEEE--

EEEEEEEEEE--

DUDE.

I SO *TOTALL* RESCUE YOU.

--SPUTTER--
KOF!

I GOTTA FIND MY *PARENTS,* MAKE SURE THEY'RE OKAY--

I SAW 'EM. THEY'RE FINE.

I JUST WANNA...WAIT A SEC, AN' SEE...

...IF ANY OF 'EM MADE IT *OUT...*

WHAT DID THEY *DO* TO YOU?

THEY... WANTED ME TO *JOIN* 'EM. THEY SAW SOMETHIN' O' *ME* IN THEM.

AIN'T MANY WHO'LL *ADMIT* THAT. AND FOR A *BIT,* THERE...

WHAT MAKES YOU THINK WE DO?

UM, LIKE... ...EVERYTHING.

WELL, YOU MISUNDERSTAND.

LOGAN AND I HAVE A GREAT DEAL OF *RESPECT* FOR EACH OTHER'S FIELD EXPERIENCE AND COMMITMENT TO *MUTANT RIGHTS*.

REALLY?

HAVE YOU EVER ACTUALLY *TALKED* TO LOGAN?

AAAGH!! DUDE!!

GROSS!!

SSSSSHH!!

I WILL NOT "SSSHHH!!"

THAT DISGUSTING BARNACLE THING TOTALLY GOT SLIME ALL OVER MY UNIFORM!!

KREEEEEEEEEE-

KWAAAAASH

QUAAASH

RRAAAHHH!! GET OFF!!

HEHH

HEHH

HEHH

GREAT...

OOOH! SOMETHING [PERFE]CT-PERFECT [C]OPS CAN'T DO!

WHAT MAKES YOU SO HIGH AND MIGHTY, ANYWAY?

I'VE BEEN AN X-MAN LONGER THAN ANYONE.

SINCE I WAS YOUR AGE, IN FACT.

AND IT STILL TOOK ME A LONG TIME TO LEARN...

"...WHAT CAN HAPPEN IF YOU'RE CARELESS. IF YOU DON'T FOLLOW THE RULES.

"UNLIKE WOLVERINE, I'M NOT INVULNERABLE."

AND NEITHER ARE YOU.

SO YOU WILL OBEY MY ORDERS.

MY EYEBEAMS CAN'T DENT THESE DOORS-- CAN YOU PHASE THROUGH?

BJEEEEEEEEEEWM

NO--IT'S GOT THE SAME PROTECTION AS THE WALLS!

AND THEY'RE LOCKED FROM THE OTHER SIDE!

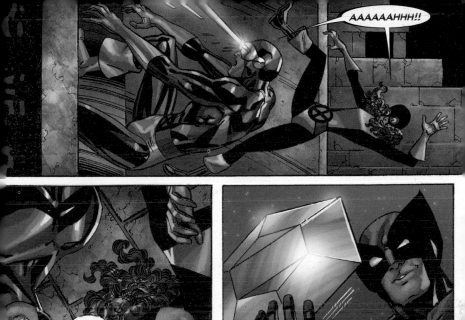

FIVE MINUTES INTO YOUR FIRST *TRAINING SESSION* AND YOU NEARLY UNLEASH *ARMAGEDDON,* CYKE?

CAN'T SAY I'M *SURPRISED.*

HOW YOU AND THE REST O' YOUR *"FIRST CLASS"* KEPT YOURSELVES *ALIVE* BEFORE I CAME ALONG I GOT *NO IDEA*--

WHY DON'T YOU LEAVE CYCLOPS ALONE FOR ONCE, HUH?!

HE'S BEEN THROUGH A *LOT!*

DON'T LOOK AT ME.

KITTY?

DID YOU DISCOVER THE SOURCE OF THAT SOUND?

THIS IS A *JOB.* IT'S NOT *ME.*

I WANT TO WEAR A *UNIFORM.*

NOT A *COSTUME.*

SO I'D RATHER STAY *WOLVERINE'S* STUDENT, IF THAT'S OKAY.

OF COURSE. AS YOU WISH.

I'M BEAT. I'M GONNA TURN IN.

GOOD NIGHT, KITTY.

IT'S SAFE TO COME OUT NOW.

LITTLE SQUIRT...

END

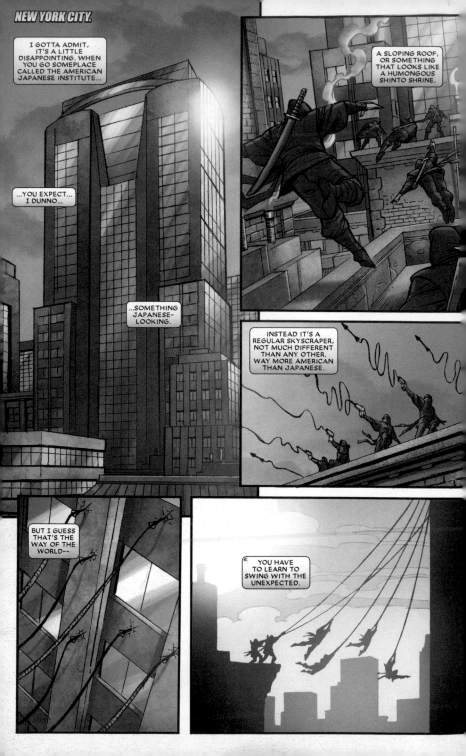

SMOOTH, SARAH. *REALLY* SMOOTH.

COULD YOU STOP DOING THAT PLEASE?

HOW CAN YOU SEE ME DOING IT IF YOU'RE REALLY *BLIND?*

I *CAN'T* SEE IT. BUT I CAN STILL FEEL *BREEZE* IN MY FACE.

ARE YOU TRYING TO MAKE ME EMBARRASSED TO BE SEEN WITH YOU?

AT LEAST *HE* DIDN'T SEE ME WITH YOU.

OHMIGOSH. DO YOU HAVE *ANY* FILTER BETWEEN YOUR HEAD AND YOUR MOUTH? *BESIDES,* DON'T YOU RECOGNIZE HIM?

THAT'S MATT MURDOCK. HE'S, LIKE, THIS FAMOUS BLIND LAWYER.

"MY HUSBAND WAS A GREAT MAN, BUT THERE WERE SOME DISREPUTABLE INDIVIDUALS WITH WHOM HE DID NOT HESITATE TO DO BUSINESS.

"WHEN HE PASSED AWAY FROM CANCER LAST MONTH, I TOOK OVER THE COMPANY AND MADE CLEAR TO THOSE INDIVIDUALS THAT THEIR BUSINESS WAS NO LONGER WELCOME.

"THEY DID NOT TAKE IT WELL. FIRST THEY CLAIMED I WAS 'BLOWING SMOKE,' AS THEY PUT IT...

"...AND THEN THEY SAID THAT MY DECISION WOULD NOT STAND. THAT AS A 'MERE WOMAN,' I COULD NOT HOPE TO COMPREHEND THE COMPLEXITIES OF THE WORLD.

"THEY MADE CLEAR THE RO WOULD DRO IN ON ME."

LOGAN'S NOWHERE AROUND. WHERE COULD HE BE?

IS THIS WHAT BEING ONE OF THE X-MEN IS LIKE? IT USED TO BE THAT I COULD GO TO MUSEUMS OR CONCERTS OR AMUSEMENT PARKS WITHOUT THINKING I WAS UNDER ATTACK--

--MUCH LESS BEING RIGHT ALL THE TIME.

KITTY?

STAY HERE.

BUT WHERE ARE YOU--?

IF HE'S NOT OUT HERE, WOL--LOGAN MUST STILL BE IN THE BUILDING.

I'M GOING TO FIND HIM.

THEY CLOSED UP! HOW WILL YOU GET IN?

NOT A PROBLEM FOR SOMEONE WHO CAN PHASE THROUGH ANYTHING.

I JUST HOPE I'M WRONG ABOUT ALL THIS. HECK, MAYBE LOGAN'S JUST OFF SOMEWHERE QUIET, SIPPING TEA WITH SOMEONE.

YEAH, RIGHT. THAT'LL BE THE DAY.

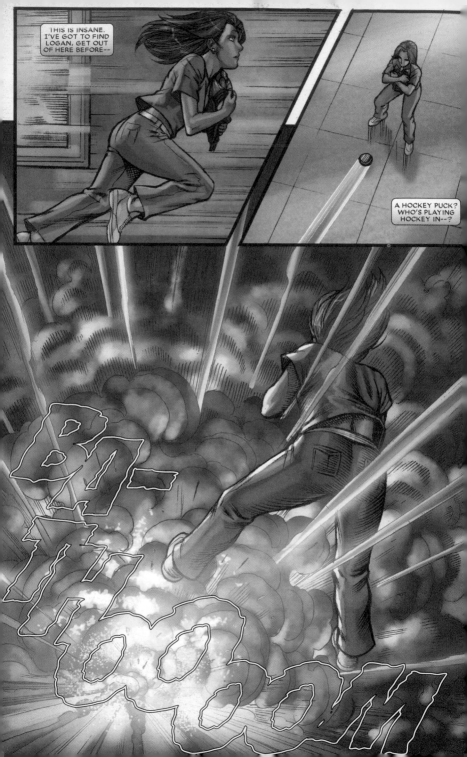

"LIVING UP" TO ANYTHING WILL NO LONGER BE A CONCERN FOR YOU. FOR ANY OF YOU.

VE TO TIME PERFECTLY. IF N'T...SARAH'S ONE FOR.

ASE MY FIST OUGH, HARDEN JUST ENOUGH KNOCK THE ASK FREE...

WHA--?

HOW DARE YOU!!!!

Y'THINK THAT'S BAD? HERE'S WORSE NEWS:

K-KITTY?

YOU OKAY, SARAH? A GAS MAIN EXPLODED AND YOU PASSED OUT FROM THE EXCITEMENT.

PASSED OUT--?

YUP.

I COULD SWEAR THERE WERE SOME... SOME PEOPLE IN COSTUMES...

NOPE. NOBODY LIKE THAT HERE.

YOU POSITIVE?

ABSO-TOOTLY.

CAN... CAN WE GO HOME NOW?

SURE.

THAT WAS GUTSY, THE WAY YA STOOD UP TO ME BEFORE.

THANKS.

DON'T MAKE A HABIT OF IT.

YESSIR.

YOU THINK SHE'S GOING TO REMEMBER ANY OF IT?

NOT IF WE'RE LUCKY. THEN AGAIN, THERE'S NO PREDICTING MEMORY.

FER INSTANCE, I KEEP THINKIN' THERE'S SOMETHING I'M FORGETTING. SOMETHING IMPORTANT.

"AH WELL. IT'LL PROBABLY COME T'ME."

PANG PANG PANG

LOGAN? ELEKTRA? IS IT SAFE TO COME OUT YET?

HELLO?

HELLO?

END

--CLOSER?

TrAWAAAAAMMMm

ROCK GODS

PETER
DAVID
writer

SCOTT
KOBLISH
artist

ULISES
ARREOLA
colorist

VC's JOE
CARAMAGNA
letterer/production

CALERO &
SOTOCOLO
cover

RALPH
MACCHIO
consulting

NATHAN
COSBY
editor

JOE
QUESADA
editor in chief

DAN
BUCKLEY
publisher

ALAN
FINE
exec. produc

PLEEEEEEE--

--EEEEEEEEEEEE--

--EEEEEEEEEEE--

--EEEEEEEEASSSSE?

VAT DOES SHE *WANT?*

SHE WANTS ME TO--

Y'KNOW, I ACTUALLY DON'T *REMEMBER.*

I WANT TO *FIX* IT SO FRIENDS AND CAN MEET *THOR!*

I *TOLD* YOU, I DON'T *KNOW* THE GUY!

THOR, THE *THUNDER* GOD?

NO, THOR HEYERDAHL.

ACTUALLY, *THAT* I COULD ARRANGE. HE OWES ME FOR HELPING HIM BUILD THE KON-TIKI.

EVEN IF OU HAVEN'T HIM, HE *MUST* OW WHO YOU RE! I MEAN YOU'RE...

...YOU'RE... ...*YOU!*

SHE'S GOT YOU THERE. YOU *ARE* YOU.

THAT'S A RELIEF.

KITTY, IF YOU DON'T MIND MY ASKING, VHY THE SUDDEN OBSESSION WITH THOR?

IT'S NOT AN OBSESSION! IT'S JUST THAT HE'S, Y'KNOW... *HOT.*

LUCKY THING HE CAN WHIP UP A RAIN-STORM AND COOL DOWN.

LOGAN, SERIOUSLY--

SERIOUSLY, THEN: WHERE'S THIS *COMIN'* FROM? ARE YOU TRYING TO IMPRESS THOSE GIRLS AT THE DANCE SCHOOL AGAIN?

NO.

OKAY, FINE! I WANTED TO PRESS THEM! SUE! THOR'S, LIKE, THE ROCK GOD OF SUPERGUYS!

AND HE'S APPEARING AT CITY HALL IN MANHATTAN TOMORROW. ACCEPTING SOME KIND OF MEDAL OF HONOR.

YOU CAN *INTRODUCE* ME.

INTRO--? I DON'T *BELIEVE* IT. YOU'RE INTIMIDATED BY HIM!

I AM *NOT!*

YOU *ARE!*

OKAY, I AM! SO WILL YOU--?

NO.

FINE! I HAVE JUST LISTENED TO *JEAN!*

SHE TOLD ME TO ASK *SCOTT* TO DO IT! BECAUSE HE'S *NICE!* AND HE'S CARING!

THAT'S WHY SHE LOVES HIM SO MUCH!

SO *ASK* HIM.

MAYBE I *WILL.*

MAYBE YOU *DID.*

MAYBE I *DID!*

AND HE ALREADY SAID NO.

MAYBE HE--

YEAH, HE SAID NO.

I'VE NEVER FELT LIKE SUCH A DOPE. LOGAN JUST FLOATS THERE, STARING AT ME, FOR ALMOST A MINUTE. AND THEN...

HEH.

OKAY.

O-OKAY? YOU MEAN YOU'LL *DO* IT?

YEAH.

BUT...

I DON'T MEAN TO LOOK A GIFT HORSE IN, Y'KNOW, THE MOUTH, BUT--

WHY?

BECAUSE YA MADE ME *LAUGH.*

OH.

UH...

NO PROBLEM.

LOGAN COULDN'T UNDERSTAND.

I MEAN, I CAN PHASE THROUGH *ANYTHING*, BUT *NOTHING* FAZES HIM.

I DON'T THINK HE WAS EVER A KID. HE WAS PROBABLY *BORN* FORTY YEARS OLD.

SO...SO HOW DO WE GET *NEAR* HIM, LOGAN?

EASY. I POP MY CLAWS AND HACK A PATH.

THEN YOU PHASE THROUGH THE RUNNING, SCREAMING PEOPLE, AND I'LL INTRODUCE YOU.

C'MON, LOGAN, SERIOUSLY...

SERIOUSLY? SOMETHING'LL COME UP.

HUH?

TRUST ME. I BEEN DOING THIS LONGER THAN YOU. LONGER THAN *ANYBODY* 'CEPT *THAT* GUY UP THERE.

I STILL DON'T UNDER-STAND WHY YOU--

DID'JA WONDER WHY I TOLD'JA TO WEAR YOUR *COSTUME* UNDER YOUR CLOTHES?

YES, BUT--

'ERE'D GO?!?

WHERE ELSE DO GODS GO? UP.

WHAT HAPPENED DOWN *THERE*?

I'M HONESTLY NOT SURE. I THINK I HELPED HIM SOMEHOW.

GET A CHANCE TO TELL HIM ABOUT YOUR *"FRIENDS?"*

NO. AND EVEN IF I HAD... COMPARED TO THE WHOLE *"MAJESTIC"* THING HE HAD GOING, IT SEEMED KINDA... I DUNNO...

...SMALL.

WE DON'T GET TO SEE THE END OF THOR'S FIGHT WITH *WHATEVER-THAT-WAS.* THEY PROBABLY TOOK IT TO ASGARD OR SOMETHING.

BUT I'M SURE THOR HANDED HIS HEAD TO HIM.

THOR'S DAY

JUST LIKE WHITNEY AND HER PALS ARE GOING TO DO WHEN I GO BACK TO CLASS.

GEE, KITTY. ANOTHER DAY, ANOTHER NO-SHOW FROM THOR. HE LOSE YOUR PHONE NUMBER?

FINE, YOU WIN. I WAS LYING. HAPPY?

MS. HUNTER DANCE ACADEMY
ONE FLI

TEASE THEM NOT SO, KATHERINE. IN TRUTH, THE PHONE NUMBER WAS LOST IN A TRAGIC... AH...

...FROST GIANT ATTACK.

BE THESE THY FRIENDS? WHAT FORTUNE THAT THEY BASK IN YOUR PRESENCE!

ABSOLUTELY. WE CAN'T GET ENOUGH OF HER. RIGHT, KITTY?

RIIIIIIIGHT. UH...THOR... HOW DID YOU FIND ME IF YOU, UH...LOST MY NUMBER?

HOW LONG DOES IT TAKE YOU TO GET YOUR HAIR LOOKING SO GOOD?

MINE... HAIR?

A MUTUAL FRIEND TRACKED ME DOWN. HE PURPORTS TO BE THE BEST THERE IS AT SUCH THINGS.

SO...IT HAS BEEN SOME TIME, KATHERINE. IS THERE ANYTHING ON THY MIND?

HEH.

THAT KID CRACKS ME UP.

ACTUALLY, YEAH. I WAS WONDERING...

END

"DIE? SOMEONE WROTE 'DIE' IN OUR DRESSING ROOM?"

BEDAZZLED

PETER DAVID: WRITER • GURIHIRU: ARTISTS
VC'S RUS WOOTON: LETTERER/PRODUCTION • WILLIAMS & STRAIN: COVER
RALPH MACCHIO: CONSULTING • NATHAN COSBY: EDITOR • JOE QUESADA: EDITOR IN CHIEF
DAN BUCKLEY: PUBLISHER • ALAN FINE: EXECUTIVE PRODUCER

KITTY PRYDE WANTS TO BECOME ONE OF THE MUTANT SUPER HERO
X-MEN, BUT SHE'LL HAVE TO SURVIVE AS THE ORIGINAL MEMBER OF...

WOLVERINE
FIRST CLASS

I AM, WOLVERINE!

YOU'RE? WOLVERINE?

NO, I'M ALISON BLAIRE! MAKE UP YER MIND.

WHY IS HE HERE?

I LIVE HERE. WHY'RE YOU HERE?

WOLVERINE'S SENSE OF HUMOR REQUIRES SOME GETTING USED TO.

FORTUNATELY YOU'LL HAVE PLENTY OF OPPORTUNITY TO DO SO.

PARDON?

'SCUSE ME?

SOMEONE HAS EXPRESSED A DESIRE TO EXTERMINATE DAZZLER.

MAYBE THEY HEARD HER SING.

HEY!

ARETHA FRANKLIN AIN'T LOSING ANY SLEEP. I'M JUST SAYIN'.

WOLVERINE, I'D LIKE YOU TO ACCOMPANY DAZZLER. KEEP AN EYE ON HER UNTIL WE CAN DETERMINE THE NATURE OF THE THREAT.

FORGET IT! TEN MINUTES WITH HIM, I'LL KILL MYSELF!

DON'T WORRY, I HAVE SOMEONE IN MIND TO ACT AS BUFFER. I SUSPECT SHE'LL BE MORE ENTHUSED ABOUT THE ASSIGNMENT.

YES! YES! YES! YES!

SAINTS, KITTY, WHAT'S GOING ON?!

I'M GOING TO BE BODY-GUARDING *DAZZLER*, TERRY! AT THE *MEGA BOWL!*

DAZZLER?!

YES!

THE *SINGER!?*

YES! YOU'RE GOING TO BE RIGHT BACKSTAGE AND EVERYTHING?! AT THE MEGA BOWL?!?

YES!

DID THE PROFESSOR ASSIGN YOU?

YES!

I WANT IN!

YES!

NO!

THIS IS *MY GIG!*

SIRYN DOESN'T GET TO HORN IN ON *MY GIG!* NO WAY!

DID YE SAY YE LOST A BACKUP SINGER?

YUP.

I'LL KILL HER. WHAT PART OF *"FOLLOW MY LEAD"* WAS UNCLEAR?

BECAUSE I SING A LITTLE. I'M TOLD I HAVE A PRETTY GOOD VOICE.

YEAH? HIT ME WITH YOUR BEST SHOT.

NO ONE'S HITTING *ANYONE* WITH ANYTH--

♫ AMA-ZING GRAAACE, HOW SWEET THE SOUND THAT SAVED A WRETCH LIKE MEEEEE... ♫

OH MY GOD.

SO WHO YA ROOTIN' FOR?

WHAT DO YOU MEAN?

IT'S THE SEA-EAGLES VERSUS THE COLOSSAL. WHO DO YA THINK WILL WIN?

COLOSSAL.

WHY?

BECAUSE SEA-EAGLES ARE BIRDS AND COLOSSAL IS GIGANTIC. SO BIG STUFF CAN CRUSH BIRDS

÷ HUFF ÷
÷ HUFF ÷

YOU KNOW, YOU *COULD* HELP ME CARRY THIS.

SORRY. GOTTA KEEP MY HANDS FREE.

NEVER KNOW WHEN I GOTTA LEAP INTO ACTION.

YOU'RE ENJOYING THIS WAY TOO MUCH!

OKAY, ALI! SOUND CHECK'S GOOD!

LET'S CLEAR OUT, GET YOU INTO COSTUME, AND WAIT FOR OUR BIG MOMENT.

YEAH. I HEAR THERE'S GONNA BE A FOOTBALL GAME HERE.

WHO LOOKS *GOOD* TO YA, DAZ?

SEA-EAGLES BY SIX POINTS.

YER *KIDDIN'*. SEA-EAGLES HAVE THE BEST DEFENSE IN THE LEAGUE.

AND WHEN YOU LOOK AT THE COLOSSAL OFFENSIVE STATS...

ERALL, AYE, BUT EY'VE BEEN ON A R THE PAST FOUR EEKS. THEY'RE A YOUNG TEAM AND THEY'RE HUNGRY

KITTY, BACK ME UP ON THIS.

YOU WERE SUPPOSED TO BACK *ME* UP.

I THINK THE SEA-EAGLES ARE GOING TO SCRATCH THE COLOSSALS' EYES OUT.

INTERESTING PICK SYSTEM.

IT'S ACTUALLY PRETTY FLEXIBLE.

THIS TOTALLY STINKS

WHAT AM I EVEN *DOING* HERE? OR EVEN WITH THE X-MEN?

WITH ALL THE POWER THEY HAVE-- WEATHER CONTROL, AND SUPER-STRENGTH, AND METAL CLAWS...

AND THEN THERE'S ME. I CAN PHASE THROUGH STUFF. *WHOOPEE.*

HOW'S OUR GIRL?

YOU MEAN DAZZLER? FINE.

GOOD. I'VE GOT A LOT WRAPPED UP IN HER.

WHAT DO YOU MEAN?

I MEAN BEING HER MANAGER HAS BECOME MY WHOLE LIFE. I USED TO HAVE A BOYFRIEND, HOBBIES, A WHOLE OTHER EXISTENCE.

AND NOW MY LIFE IS DAZZLER, TWENTY-FOUR/SEVEN.

AND DO YOU *RESENT* HER FOR IT?

OF COURSE NOT.

WELL...

MAYBE A *LITTLE.* SOMETIMES IT'S EASY TO RESENT PEOPLE, Y'KNOW?

YEAH. I KNOW.